ABOUT THE AUTHOR

After graduating from UCL in '03 with a Degree in Statistics & Economics, Sean Smithson accidentally became a tax adviser for a wealth management firm in London. Following a number of failed attempts to escape, he finally quit in '12 and left to see the world; hoping to find some answers about what to do next.

If his parents had their way, he'd be married, working for Goldman Sachs and living in Chelsea. But having blown most of his savings travelling, he's currently single, 'in between jobs' and freeloading at their place until he sells enough copies of this book to move out. He didn't find those answers.

However he did rediscover his passion for storytelling, and, buoyed by fellow travellers, he made the leap from pub raconteur to writer, setting up SeanSmithson.com in '13. Initially a blueprint for *How to LOSE a GIRL in 10 Ways*, it continues to grow and when Sean's not trying (and failing) to pick-up women, he's adding new stories to the site.

Sean Smithson is a pen name. Being Tamil it's far easier to pronounce than his real one but more importantly, this way, his parents will hopefully never find out what he's really like.

How to LOSE a GIRL in 10 WAYS

Words from a Wonderfully Woeful Womaniser

Sean Smithson

Matador
9 Priory Business Park
Kibworth Beauchamp
Leicestershire LE8 0RX, UK
Tel: (+44) 116 279 2299
Fax: (+44) 116 279 2277
Email: books@troubador.co.uk
Web: www.troubador.co.uk/matador

ISBN 978 1783063 857

British Library Cataloguing in Publication Data.
A catalogue record for this book is available from the British Library.

Typeset in Bembo by Troubador Publishing Ltd
Printed and bound in the UK by TJ International, Padstow, Cornwall

Matador is an imprint of Troubador Publishing Ltd

For Byron, Mellissa and Vasi.
I couldn't have done this without you.

Disclaimer

The stories you're about to read are completely genuine and took place at some point during the last ten years, whilst I was living and working in London. They are as accurate as I can remember (I was usually fairly boshed at the time) but the names of the people involved have been changed to save relationships / friendships and to prevent any potential lawsuits.

Contents

#1 – Totally misread the situation   1

#2 – Turn up with a guy who has more money than you   10

#3 – Suck at Economics   15

#4 – Watch porn   31

#5 – Forget to book a room at the hotel   39

#6 – Try to sleep with her best friend   54

#7 – Take her number down incorrectly   62

#8 – Have 'some' standards   76

#9 – Order the hot wings before your date   85

#10 – Try to give her career advice   91

Glossary   98

#1

TOTALLY MISREAD THE SITUATION

I knew from the first moment I saw her that Catherine and I were going to end up sleeping with one another. Assuming we both got offered jobs of course.

We'd made it to the second interview stage and crossed paths briefly in reception. She wasn't my usual spec (looked kind of like a librarian if you know what I mean) but beneath a very modest top it looked like she could be concealing some pretty decent bar. Plus my brother's friend had told me all about 'city girls' and how common it was to hook-up with your colleagues. And Catherine just looked like she'd be one of those girls.

She was very shy and consequently I kept my distance from her, both in and out of work. But she finally came out of her shell at our Christmas party in '04. I'd actually wanted to hook-up with one of the senior consultants, Lucy, but I ended up back at Catherine's.

It nearly didn't happen as we were both so drunk that we just went to sleep. But she accidentally woke me up later that night to get some water and I thought, *Well we're up now...*

I was expecting the 'please don't tell anyone, I have a

1

boyfriend' spiel the following Monday, but what did surprise me was her insistence that she didn't want that night to affect our friendship.

Friendship? At best we were office acquaintances. But her bar was even better than originally suspected and the sex was great. So I made sure I wasn't a total wanker just in case there was a chance of re-tap in the future.

There would be three more occasions that I ended up back at Catherine's place but only one of them is really worth telling you about.

★

Fast forward to summer '05 and another office party. As was fast becoming my *modus operandi*, I got pleasantly drunk by around 9 pm and started to contemplate who to flirt with.

Back then the department was split into two teams: A and B. All the women on my team (A) were married so that was a dead-end. On B, only three were neither engaged nor married: Catherine, Lucy (who was still not putting out) and Carrie.

I would go on to sleep with all three of them on various occasions over the years but that particular night, I was after Catherine.

Given our inability to have a conversation – which had become worse after the Christmas encounter – I really had to struggle with my opener. But looking back, I was quite impressed. Especially in light of how the conversation started.

After a textbook, "How's it going?" I offered to get her a drink.

"No thanks, I'm OK. I'm probably going to head off soon."

What? This isn't part of the script. I couldn't just steam in with a 'well how about we recreate another cock in mouth situation?' I had to think of something clever. And quick.

The last time we hooked up Catherine was staying in a bed-sit in Hammersmith. And I was still at my parents.

Me:	"Listen, I know this is going to sound odd but do you still live in Hammersmith?"
Catherine:	"Yes. But I'm in a new place with a girlfriend, why?"
Me:	"Weeell... I'd like to stick around a bit longer" – at which point, she was either disappointed that I didn't try to fish for an invite back to hers or she was incredibly relieved – "but I'm worried about getting home is all. Could I possibly get your number and call you later if I'm in a jam? I'll sleep on the couch naturally."
Catherine:	"Hmm. I guess so. So long as it's not too late. And you're definitely sleeping on the couch!"

I knew it. Clearly I should've skipped the preamble and gone straight for the cock in mouth line. "Yes, I promise it won't be too late and of course I'll be on the couch," I responded rather arrogantly.

So Catherine left and I continued drinking. It must've been around 1.30 am when I called her. I had to call late enough that she couldn't question if the trains were still running but not so late that she would've already gone to sleep.

I was also going to lie and say that I was in a cab on the way to hers, just in case she had second thoughts.

Four rings. *Dammit. I knew I should've left earlier.* I was about to hang up when a very grumpy voice mumbled, "Hey, where are you?"

Me: *Yesss!* "Oh, I'm in a cab. I asked the guy to head to Hammersmith. I hope that's OK?"

Catherine: "Erm. Yeah, I suppose so."

Me: "Cool. Thank you again. I really appreciate it."

Catherine: "Yeah sure. No worries."

Me: "What's your address by the way?"

Catherine: "Oh sorry. It's…"

★

Me: "Wow, this is a really nice flat. Much better than your last place. And didn't you say the rent was quite cheap?"

Catherine: "Yeah, it's actually my flatmate's uncle's place, which is why it's such a good deal."

Me: "Nice. Speaking of your flatmate, is she in?"

Catherine: "Erm no. I think she's at her boyfriend's place tonight."

Stop it. This night just gets better and better.

Catherine: "Well anyway, I'm really tired so I'm going to bed. The spare room is over on the right."

WHAT THE FUCK IS THIS?

Catherine: "The sheets haven't been changed in a while but we don't have too many visitors so you should be fine."

Once again, she was choosing to blatantly disregard the script. But before I could think of an appropriate response her back was turned and she was already in her room.

I sat at the foot of the bed contemplating what my next move would be and then it hit me. She was obviously playing hard to get. Why else would she give me her number, let me stay round when her flatmate was out, and more importantly, wake up and wait for me to come round just to shut me down?

So I got completely undressed and made my way to her room. *Knock, knock.*

Catherine: "Yeah, what is it? Oh my God! Where are your clothes?"

Me: "Come on now Catherine. You can cut the act."

Catherine: "I knew this was what you were after when you asked to stay round!"

And yet you still let me in didn't you?

Catherine: "But I thought I'd give you the benefit of the doubt."

Me: "Benefit of the doubt? Of course you knew this was why I wanted to come round. Listen, I know you're still with James but he never needs to know."

I tried to hold her hand but she backed away slowly and very calmly told me that she wasn't joking, the last time we hooked up was a huge mistake, that I was still welcome to use the spare room but that I was to fuck off out of her room immediately before she screamed.

Contrary to how I must be sounding right now, I wasn't a complete douche and apologised profusely for misreading (I mean, creating) the situation. I also thanked her for still agreeing to let me stay and for once, I actually begged the girl not to tell anyone about what had happened!

Within seconds I was back at that same spot on the bed thinking about the mess I'd gotten myself into. Now most guys would've bolted from there and not looked back. Or they would've at least made use of the room (it was around 2.30 am). But not me. As there is something very wrong with me.

I put my clothes back on and went into the living room. After around two minutes of shuffling through the items on her coffee table, I found what I was looking for: the local paper. I went straight to the back page and made my way forward until I hit the jackpot: 'Escort and massage services'.

I got my phone out and started dialling… Finally I found an agency based on the other side of London. However they were willing to send someone to Hammersmith. But first the admin.

Agency: "What's your address?"

What is MY address? Hell, if I remembered what Catherine said. So I thought, *Where do most people leave their mail?* I asked the guy to hold and dashed to the kitchen. Bingo. An electricity bill.

6

Me: "Erm, it's…"
Agency: "Right. It's £130 for the hour…"

Suddenly I realised that I only had about £40 on me.

Me: "Erm. I don't suppose you accept credit card, do you?"
Agency: "What do you think?"
Me: "Ah. I see."
Agency: "Listen buddy. Why don't you call me back when you've sorted yourself out. We have serious punters on hold."

Maybe I should have explained my predicament. If he knew the lengths I was prepared to go to just to get laid maybe he would've given me a discount?

Now at this point, even the very few guys who made it with me this far would've thrown in the towel. But not me. As there is something very wrong with me.

I put the phone down and this time started to shuffle through ALL of Catherine's things. What was I looking for? Cash.

Even as I write this I am appalled (secretly proud) by what I did that night. I mean, trying to nail a pro in a colleague's flat whilst she was sleeping, straight after she had just rejected you. And to top it off, I was going to steal from her in order to pay for it.

I should've stopped when I couldn't find any money and perhaps there may still have been a chance for me to get into heaven (or in my case, to be reincarnated as a king or a rock star). But instead I did the unthinkable. *Knock, knock.*

Me: "Listen Catherine, don't worry I'm not naked or anything. But I was just wondering; do you happen to have any cash on you?"

That's it. Get this man a first class ticket to Hell. I am definitely coming back as a toilet seat when my time is up.

Catherine: "Huh. Why? What for?"

Me: "Well it's actually to pay for a hooker and I only have £40. If you think about it, it's only right that you pay the rest as this is entirely your fault for being a frigid, prick teasing cow." Is what I should have said. But as I hadn't thought it through properly, what I actually came up with was, "Oh, I was thinking of getting a cab back home and don't think I have enough."

Catherine: "Sorry, I only have a fiver on me. But there's a cash machine about five minutes away on the high street."

Now I was fucked. Once I left the flat I would be completely out of options. *Hmm. How did such a promising situation turn into this?*

Whilst I stood there pondering, Catherine had put her dressing gown on and had already opened the front door to let me out.

Down trodden, humiliated and finally accepting defeat, I apologised again for what had happened earlier and made my way to the front door. But before leaving I asked to use her bathroom and had the most furious of wanks.

Perhaps if I had just done that earlier in one of the bar toilets I wouldn't have been in that situation. But then again, where's the fun in that?

On the cab ride home I kept thinking where it all went wrong; first with Catherine and then with the attempted pro. And what could I possibly have said to allow me to leave, get cash and come back to hers?

Oh and before I forget. This was the first of the three further occasions I ended up back at Catherine's. The end results on visits three and four were much, much better.

#2

Turn up with a guy who has more money than you

I must've met Christina back in '05 as I was still on the graduate programme at the time. Following a minor ticking off from management about my billable hours, John took me out to cheer me up and discuss what I could do to improve my stats.

Being the only male assistant manager at the time, I guess they figured he'd make the best mentor. Though had they have known of our mutual appreciation of booze and tits at the outset, I'm sure they would have reconsidered. We eventually ended up in Secrets, Holborn.

If I had any idea that night how many times I'd be back, I would have tried to make a better first impression. But as you'll note from the equation below, it wasn't my fault.

Woeful graduate salary + unhealthy love of brasses + student Barclaycard = Derisory strip club kitty

I wasn't quite as pathetic as I was on my strip club debut but I was still a sucker for pretty girls who showed me any sort of attention. So when John left me on my own I knew I was fucked.

A solitary minute passed before I was duped into a dance that, on reflection, was definitely a waste of money. My hope was that John would be back when Miss 'you have no chance of 'accidentally' grabbing my boobs' was done but when I returned, he was off again.

This time I stayed strong for two whole R Kelly songs and thought I was saved when he sat back down. But then SHE clocked me. For the porn enthusiasts out there, she looked a lot like a younger, pre-boob job Brandi Love.

… brief interlude while you Google Images her…

I'm not even sure that I waited for the usual sales pitch and believe I just said, "Yes please" when she made eye contact with me.

Now being super-hot is one thing but you would sooner have a seven or an eight who knew how to work it – I only found out years later that this was essentially any girl who worked at Parkers – over a ten who stood five feet away and just went through the motions. So I had to have a trial run first before deciding how much of my remaining funds I would commit (excluding cab fare and the trial run, I had about £60).

Well. Not only was she a ten, her milkshake definitely brought all the boys to the yard so I was more than happy to spend everything.

Christina: "You know, for £100 we could go to a more private booth?"

Me:	"Is THAT right?" *She is borderline dry humping me for forty sheets, surely there is an outside possibility of fingering for a hundred!* "OK do you mind waiting here? I just want to let my boss know I could be a while?" *That. And I want to ask for £40.*
Christina:	"Oh that guy was your boss was he?"
Me:	"Yeah, why?" *I genuinely had no idea how this was going to end.*
Christina:	"Oh no reason. See you in a bit."

Thankfully John was still at the table and, more surprisingly, he was on his own. I had just explained the pickle I was in and was about to ask for the money when I heard, "So you're Sean's boss are you?" *OH NO SHE DIDN'T!*

Me:	"Oh heeey…" I pretended that I was expecting her arrival. "I thought you were going to wait in the booth? Sorry. John, Christina. Christina, John."
Christina:	"Hi John." She offered out her gold-digging hand to shake his. "I was going to but then I thought I'd join you boys for a drink if that's OK?" Cue puppy-dog eyes and sultry pout. *Whore.*
John:	"Yeah, of course that's OK. What would you like?" *Mother-fucker.*

All I could think about while we sat there awkwardly waiting for our drinks was, *Yes, she's a complete money-grabbing bitch (just*

doing her job), but she's my money-grabbing bitch. I saw her first so do the right thing here John. Give me the money and walk away.
Is that what you think happened?

| John: | "Oh look the drinks are here. Listen, Sean mentioned something earlier about a private booth? Why don't we have our drinks there instead?" *OH NO HE DIDN'T!* |
| Christina: | "That sounds perfect. Have a good night sweetie." |

I tried not to look at her in case she saw the tears of rejection in my eyes and instead glared at John, with a 'dude, what the fuck?' look.

| John: | "Sorry mate, she's just too fit." *I know that you prick.* "I presume you'll be gone when I get back so erm, I'll see you at work tomorrow yeah?" |

Some bloody mentor. I was more upset now than at the beginning of the night and he never actually explained how I should be reporting my billable hours either.

★

John's head was buried in his hands the next morning – hopefully nursing an awful hangover though potentially sniffing his fingers – but that didn't stop me from reminding him what a wanker he was.

"Look mate, I'm sorry but I'm a tad fragile right now so can we do this later? Plus you should read my email as it might cheer you up."

He was right. It did.

Including cab fare and late night snacks from the Esso garage, I'd spent almost £150 that night. Which may not sound like much but was a significant dent in an already drained graduate wallet; especially for such a forgettable night.

But that was nothing compared to the £680 she had fleeced him for. Apparently he didn't even have enough for a cab and had to walk back home. Karma my friends... She's a bitch.

#3

Suck at Economics

Poitier was an old school friend of mine but we hardly ever saw one another. So on the rare occasions that we did get together it would usually end in disaster. We'd be on shots by about the fourth round and highbrow conversation about a corporate case he was working on would quickly disintegrate into schoolboy chat about sex, girls in the office we've had sex with, girls in the office we'd like to have sex with and finally – once we were suitably drunk and horny – strippers.

Hookers would eventually make their way into the topic of conversation but only at the end of the night when we were truly bolloxed.

We hung around in Dalys till about 11 pm, by which point we were both fairly mangled so when he suggested going to the Euston branch of Secrets, I was more than keen.

After a few seriously overpriced beers and similarly priced dances from some of Eastern Europe's C list, I said to him: "Why pay all this money and still end up jerking off when we get home when we can just go whoring for the same price?"

Usually I'm known to talk a lot of shit when I'm drunk but surprisingly, when it comes to paying for sex, I actually make a lot of sense. Clearly he concurred as within minutes we were outside trying to hail a cab.

Now perhaps it's the way I ask or perhaps they just don't cover this in The Knowledge, but black cab drivers seem to have no idea where any 'saunas' are in London. So your best bet in these situations is to find an unlicensed chap, most likely of Asian or African origin.

This wasn't the first time Poitier and I had been on a 'field trip' together, so when Drives started regurgitating the same rhetoric as the guy from our previous outing – "Baker Street; you will never see girls like this. Mayfair; they will take better care of you than your girlfriends" – we took it with a pinch of salt.

We drove for around five minutes before I started to tire of his bullshit so, once again, I threw my drunken voice of reason into the mix.

"Listen, wouldn't you prefer to be in familiar surroundings after we're done? You know that we'll just want to pass out as soon as we're flat-packed."

And once again, he concurred. So I made the call.

Vinnie:	"Elite Escorts, how can I help you?"
Me:	"Hi, what girls have you got available tonight?"

Now at this stage, Vinnie's response should normally have been 'where are you?' or 'what kind of girl are you after?' But having amassed quite a few 'whore miles' over the years, I was somewhat of a face (or should I say voice) amongst the Elite staff; Vinnie in particular.

Vinnie:	"Sam, is that you? How's it going?"

Oh yes, another thing. For fear that my exploits could one day be traced back to me – somewhat ironic given that I am now writing about them – I always used the alias Sam in any of my dealings with escort agencies.

Me/Sam:	"I'm good. Listen, I'm actually going to need two girls tonight as I'm with my chum."
Vinnie:	"No problem Sam. We can take care of you guys. Where are you now?"
Me/Sam:	"We're not too far from Waterloo but we're heading to Wimbledon."
Poitier:	"Drives, how long to get to Wimbledon?"
Drives:	"Maybe forty-five minutes."
Me/Sam:	"Vinnie, Drives reckons he can get to Wimbledon in forty-five minutes. Can you send the girls over in an hour or so?"
Vinnie:	"No problem. So what kind of girls are you guys after?"

At the time of this story, perhaps naively, I completely trusted Vinnie's judgement.

Me:	"Poitier, what kind of girls do you prefer?"
Poitier:	"Look Smithson, provided a man doesn't turn up at the door, I will drill anything."
Me:	"Erm Vinnie, I think we're going to leave this one totally up to you."

Now for those of you – and I imagine there are many – that are unfamiliar with the mechanics behind ordering 'take away' as my friend, Nova calls it, it's essentially the same as ordering a regular take away; you 'place your order' (the conversation we just had) and 'wait for delivery'.

Placing your Order

It's all pretty much bullshit. For Vinnie and his friends, it's all about quick turnaround, as the more girls in and out of their office on bookings, the more cash for all involved. But in order for that to happen, they need two things:

1. Callers – Smithson, Poitier... any other pissed-up losers, please step forward; and
2. To be able to convince those callers that one of the remaining girls in the office is just the right one for them.

Now clearly there'll be no shortage of callers. Hell, at one stage I reckon I was responsible for about 5% of their weekly phone traffic! But to achieve the second part, they rely on two certainties: the fact that you are drunk, horny and desperate – otherwise you wouldn't be calling them at two in the morning – and that even if you ask for a petite blonde with cracking bar, as Poitier said earlier, so long as it's not a man you'll still probably tap whoever turns up as you just want to get your end away.

Never mind that the petite blonde may actually be on her way back to the office. You're going to get whoever is available at that moment as that's another girl out the door. In layman's terms, it's similar to ordering a Meat Feast but receiving a

Hawaiian I guess. Completely different but you'll still eat it if you're hungry enough.

Their only real quandary is whether or not to tell you at the time of booking that the girl you've asked for is nothing like the one you're going to get, or to simply leave that surprise for when you open your front door.

Needless to say, I've been bowled a fair few googlies in my time. Of course this was back when my 'frequent flyer' status was still in question. Like when I asked for the 'mature, English blonde with big breasts' and was sent a twenty-four-year-old, *lactating*, Polish girl? She became very shy and backed away when I tried to suck on her nipples and when I asked what the problem was, she responded, "For the baby" and proceeded to squeeze her right breast and squirt milk out across the floor.

Naturally I couldn't do anything with her after that. And we actually spent the remainder of the hour looking through pictures of her son on her iPhone! True story.

But, over the years, you learn to accept that the term 'mature' could in fact mean any age between twenty and fifty. Also that the term 'young' could in fact mean any age between twenty and fifty. That 'gorgeous' or 'stunning' very rarely mean gorgeous or stunning. That brunette can sometimes mean blonde (and vice versa). And that Spanish could also mean French; English could mean Polish; Italian could mean Greek and so on.

Though to be fair to the guys at Elite and other agencies with no online presence, it is pretty hard when you're selling blind. And in truth, for me, part of the fun was always waiting to see just who was going to turn up.

★

I had no idea how long Poitier and I had been asleep in the back but Drives woke us up just as we were approaching the final bend before my parents' house.

Now I'm sure a lot of you will have read that last sentence and are now thinking, 'this guy's parents must no longer have been living there right?' or 'perhaps they were away on holiday as surely no decent son would be planning on having a foursome in his parents' home whilst they were actually there?'

Well I can tell you two things:

1. Poitier and I are close but not that close. Back at Waterloo, Vinnie had suggested an 'Italian brunette in her late twenties' for me and a 'petite, Czech blonde' for Poitier. We'd definitely be in separate rooms though; and
2. My mother was there.

I wish I could tell you that this was the first time I had attempted such an outlandish move but I'm afraid that wasn't the case. Indeed, so good was I at sneaking these girls in and out of my parents' house that it wasn't even a concern of mine when I made bookings. I guess if I ever got caught, my plan was always to say that that particular 'lady' was my girlfriend. And I'd address the more pressing issue of having a female sleep round the next day. Remember, I'm Tamil; a girl that isn't your fiancée or wife sleeping round is a total faux pas.

I'll explain how it all used to work but for now, just know that the two of us were about to have sex with two hookers in my parents' house whilst my mum was sleeping upstairs.

We turned the corner and Drives started to slow down as he kept an eye out for the house. We were still about fifty meters away when I suddenly noticed a silver Mercedes in the driveway and three people huddled together around the car.

Me: "Oh fuck, oh fuck, oh fuck! Poitier. The hookers are already here!"
Poitier: "Oh shit! Drives, how long were we driving for?"
Drives: "I don't know. I think maybe an hour. A lot of traffic tonight."

I looked at my phone and there were already two missed calls from the agency, one of which was at least ten minutes ago.

Me: "Fuck. Bollocks. Shit. Fuck! Drives pull over here, it's fine. I need a moment to think about this."

Poitier and I got out of the cab just outside my neighbour's house, paid Drives and just stood there for a while. My heart was pounding out of my chest at this point as I'd naturally assumed that the girls would have knocked on the front door and woken my mum up.

When I was bragging earlier about being a dab hand at 'hooker smuggling' that was because my mum or whoever else may have been there at the time was fast asleep. And more importantly, I was already in the fucking house! I had no contingency plan for this.

Usually, it's supposed to go something like…

Waiting for Delivery – the twenty step plan

1. Get home. Open gate and leave unlocked.
2. Slowly walk down path to front door.
3. Slowly open door, avoiding unnecessary key rustling.
4. Remove shoes. Instead of closing door, place one shoe on either side of open door.

Remaining tasks to be performed on tiptoe:

5. Assess the situation. If coast is clear, find quietest part of house and 'place your order'.
6. Go upstairs. Grab bed sheets, duvet, tooth brush and toothpaste.
7. Return downstairs. Brush teeth and perform general 'spring clean'.
8. Create makeshift bed.
9. Find spot next to window with view of gate and wait.
10. RESIST URGE TO GO TO SLEEP*

Once the car has pulled up outside:

11. Remove shoes from around door. Slowly walk back to gate.
12. Meet and greet with hooker. In the extremely unlikely event that you are unsatisfied with your order, phone agency to discuss alternatives. UNSURPRISINGLY, THIS HAS NEVER HAPPENED TO ME.
13. Notify her of present situation and consequent noise

restrictions. If she is uncomfortable with this, phone agency to discuss alternatives. UNSURPRISINGLY, THIS HAS NEVER HAPPENED TO ME.

Assuming steps 12 & 13 pose no problems:

14. Decide if you want to extend booking. Wait for her to confirm timings with agency.
15. Slowly lead her down path to front door, suggesting she walk on grass to avoid stiletto clatter.
16. Repeat step 4.
17. Point out where bathroom is located. Consider offering her a drink.
18. Lead her to makeshift bed and close door.
19. Pay her.
20. Do. Your. Thing.

*   This is possibly the most important step as if you nod off and the girl turns up, you're pretty much in the same position that Poitier and I were in that night.

Some years after this story, when I was living in Earl's Court, this did actually happen to me. And as I hadn't specified my flat number, the girl was unable to contact me and had to go back to the 'office'. I woke up the next morning with my phone on my chest and seven missed calls.

I definitely dropped down a tier in the 'whore miles' programme after that.

Oh, and in case there are any cynics reading this that think I'm making this up as they must have my details on a central system, just remember, they can't even afford a website. And even I've got one of those.

★

Poitier and I talked it over and decided that there were two clear exit strategies at that point. One option was to act very surprised at seeing them on the driveway; deny any knowledge of Sam or of ordering any brasses and just continue on to the house.

The downside with this approach was that Vinnie and the others knew my voice well. So a move such as that would jeopardise any future bookings. And let's face it, there would be future bookings.

The alternative was to reveal myself as Sam, apologise for the current situation, offer Drives some money for his troubles and continue on to the house.

Clearly we chose the latter.

They'd seen us standing on the pavement talking and looking in their direction so were clearly expecting us to come over. I was the first to approach them.

Me:	"Hookers right?" was my stupid opening, as I waved my index finger at the two girls and hoped by some miracle they just happened to be complete strangers who had ended up in our driveway.
Italian:	"Sam?"
Me:	"Erm yeah, that's me," I smiled nervously back at her. "This is my friend… erm… John (I'm not sure that Poitier actually has a hooker alias).

	Listen. You didn't happen to knock on the door already did you?"
Italian:	"Yes of course."
Me:	"Shiiit."
Italian:	"We rang the bell and a man answered."
Me:	"A man?" I looked over at Poitier somewhat confused initially and quickly realised that it would've been my brother coming back for the weekend. *Thank God for that.* "Oh yeah, OK. What did he say?"
Italian:	"He said that there was no one called Sam living here and that we must have the wrong address."
Me:	"OF COURSE. You would've asked for Sam, wouldn't you? Thank fuck for that stupid alias." I turned, grinning like a kid, to face Poitier to see if he too had computed the importance of the Italian's statement.

He just smiled back at me and nodded his head.

We apologised for the confusion and proceeded to work our way through steps 12 to 15. Rather than enter the house all at the same time, I suggested that the three of them wait outside whilst I did a quick recky.

It proved a very wise decision as my mum was still up, clearly perturbed by what had happened earlier. I could hear her footsteps above me and ran upstairs to intercept her before she could make it down.

Me:	"Hey Mum, it's just me. Sorry. Did I wake you?"

Mum:	"It's OK, I was up already. Listen, did you notice some women outside when you came home?"
Me:	"Nooo… Why?"
Mum:	"It was the strangest thing. Two women rang the doorbell about half an hour ago looking for someone. Thankfully your brother was here and he told them they must have had the wrong address. I was really quite scared."

Although it genuinely bothered me seeing my mum visibly shaken by all of this, I had come this far and couldn't pull the plug now. And in the back of my mind, I couldn't help wondering if she knew what I was up to and was trying to outfox me.

When I look back on that night now, I'm certain that she had absolutely no idea but I was clearly clutching at straws at the time to justify my actions. I know what you're thinking. Son of the year, right?

Me:	"Hmmm, that is strange. Especially at this time. But yeah, I guess they must've just got the wrong address. Just try to forget about it and go back to sleep." I was praying she wouldn't ask any more questions… "Oh yeah, I was out with Poitier tonight and told him he could crash here. I hope that's OK?"
Mum:	"Sure, no problem. But where will he sleep?"
Me:	"Oh he'll be fine downstairs, don't worry. In

	fact, the two of us will be up chatting for a
	bit and I'll probably crash down there too."
Mum:	"Well OK then, I'll see you guys in the
	morning."
Me:	"Yep, good night."

What a turnaround of events. We were now firmly back on track and Mum wouldn't think it odd if she heard noises from downstairs as she knew Poitier was there. My brother was fast asleep. The only loose end now was to let the others in.

I hadn't really had a chance to check the spec until then. But it was safe to say that Vinnie had excelled himself. As Poitier was technically a guest, I suggested that he use the living room and I lead the Italian to my dad's study.

With all the earlier confusion I was unable to complete step 8 so we kind of stood around awkwardly for the first five minutes making inane conversation. I've tried really hard since to remember but the next twenty-five to thirty minutes are a complete blank.

All I can recall was that things seemed to be moving at a glacial pace so I figured that she was either:

1. A lesbian – possible but probably unlikely;
2. Not that into to me – possible but probably unlikely; or
3. One of those girls that prolonged all the peripheral shit in order to try and avoid actually having sex – very possible and very likely.

I'd come across girls like this before and always made it a point to remember their names so I would say no if they were ever recommended to me again. Clearly I would have to add her to the list. That being said, I wouldn't have viewed it as a waste of money if we didn't actually fuck. After the night I'd had, a blowjob or even a hand-shandy would have sufficed. But she didn't seem to be forthcoming with either. And to add to my frustration, all I could hear from the other side of the wall were the muffled screams of Poitier destroying his little Czech girl.

At some point during her cock teasing master class she asked me what I did for a living. *LIGHT BULB.*

I figured that if I told her I was a hot shot banker (that was temporarily staying at his mum's house) she would see me as some sort of cash piñata and perhaps the potential for some extra spending money would spring her into action.

Me: "I'm a banker."
Italian: "Wow. Really?"

JACKPOT! I thought to myself as I began to take my 'recently brought back to life' penis out of my boxers.

Italian: "So, do you think the Turkish Lira is going to appreciate or depreciate against sterling over the next few years."
Me: "Erm… I'm sorry, what?" I almost laughed in disbelief.
Italian: "The Turkish Lira. Will it strengthen or weaken against the pound?"
Me: "Yes, no. I understood what you were asking me the first time. And wait a second, not that I even know or care about the answer to your

28

earlier question, but aren't you Italian? Why are you asking about the Lira?" At this point, my penis could best be described as mildly turgid.

Italian: "No, I am from Turkey."

Vinnie. You. Mother. Fucker. Do the 'miles' not count for anything?

Turk: "I have been saving my money in the UK and plan to buy some land back home. But I am not sure if I should convert my pounds now or wait to see if they will appreciate against the Lira."

OK where is Ashton Kutcher because I'm clearly getting punked right now. Is this bitch seriously asking me about exchange rate movements?

My penis was fading. And fast... *Perhaps if I could just steer her back on track.*

Me: "OK so I may have given you the wrong impression earlier when I said I was a banker. I do work in the financial industry. But I actually provide tax advice to clients. I have absolutely no experience with currency markets. So... about that blowjob?"

Turk: "Ohhh I see. But still, do you think I am being silly by waiting?"

MAN DOWN. I repeat. We have a man down.

My penis had all but disappeared by that stage and although it had been a complete fucking disaster of a night, I did still manage to crack a little smile as I realised that the night was going to end in precisely the manner I told Poitier it wouldn't: I'd spent all that money and was still going to end up jerking off.

★

My brother was still half asleep when we entered his room in the morning but as soon as he saw Poitier he smiled knowingly.

"Ohhh, you're here too. Now it all makes sense. When I opened the front door and saw two girls I thought, hmm I know Sean's a deviant but two's a bit punchy even for him. But having seen your face it all falls in to place."

I proceeded to tell them both about my night and how, in spite of my lack of action, I'd actually wished the Turk well in her future property endeavours. And through tears of laughter, my brother turned to Poitier and asked if he'd had a more successful evening. To which, he simply responded, "Smell my fingers."

What a wanker. Oh no wait. That's me.

#4

WATCH PORN

I don't know what it is but there's just something about posh girls that intimidates me and, as such, I'm rendered more bumbling and incapable around them than usual.

Maybe it's because they have supper instead of dinner? Perhaps it's just some weird fascination dating back to colonial times? Or maybe it's because to date, I've had limited to no success with any polo watching, Mulberry handbag wearing, supper eating women and my confidence around those who fit this description has understandably taken a beating.

Note; I say limited as I actually ended up in bed with one such girl after a work function. But for the life of me, I can't remember if we had sex. Or did anything for that matter; yet we both woke up without our clothes on?

Like I said, more bumbling and incapable than usual!

So when Sophie, a History student from Bristol University arrived on a summer internship in '09 before her final year, I 'planned' to keep a fairly low profile.

But it seems Loki had other ideas in store for me, as she ended up in the department directly above mine. And not only were the doors to my room made of glass, my seat faced them so we inevitably ended up gazing at one other every time she was on the staircase.

OK, I ended up gazing every single time. She would look back every so often.

This 'not so undercover' surveillance operation continued fruitlessly for the majority of her placement. However during her penultimate week I experienced my second divine intervention.

Kate: "Who is it that you keep staring at?" (Kate sat directly opposite me.)

Me: "Erm… Sophie. That new intern in Finance?"

[Kate was one of the few girls that I had a genuinely platonic friendship with and refusing to believe that I could actually be so shallow and behave the way I do; she was also constantly on the lookout for a 'nice girl' to help steer me back onto the right track. Bless her.]

Kate: "Oh yeah, I know her. Very pretty. You like her, do you?"

Me: "Well I can't be certain she's 'the one' Kate but yes, I think she's very attractive."

Kate: "Well in that case, do you want to come to her leaving drinks next Thursday? It's nothing big; just us two, the other interns and my friend Elena."

Me: *A) How the hell does Kate know Sophie? B) Why do I even care about (A)? And C) Elena's a bit of a dick. But she's a bit of a dick with a huge rack, which is essentially all it will take to get Slacks on board.* "I'm there."

[Slacks was one of my oldest friends at the firm. He was also married and one of the greatest things about 'those guys' is that they live vicariously through their single friends. In fact, of the rare successes that I've had over the years, I'd say that around a third can be directly or indirectly attributed to his or Northern Monkey's (another married friend) tireless wingman work. With the latter even managing to tee me up using the infamous 'Have you met my friend?' line. So you see, it was imperative that I had at least one of them by my side.]

★

Kate was right, it wasn't anything big at all. Though admittedly we'd turned up more than fashionably late so that could also have explained the poor turnout. We grabbed some drinks and joined the others.

Kate:	"Sean, this is Sophie. Sophie, Sean."
Me:	"Yeah, I think I've seen you a few times on the staircase."
Sophie:	"Yah, I had noticed," she quipped, before swiftly returning to her vodka tonic.

Bollocks. Did she mean 'yah I had noticed, you farking pervert' or 'yah, I kind of noticed you too'? Why did I even lead with that line?

Luckily, though I'm sure quite unintentionally, Kate made a comment about the two of us working together in tax and instead of stopping the conversation dead in its tracks, it seemed to diffuse the awkward moment perfectly. And the discussion naturally shifted onto Sophie's impressions of the firm and her plans post university.

Thanks in no small part to Slacks' 'interest' in Elena, the conversation shifted again; though this time onto dating and people's preferences. I forget now precisely what was asked of Elena but the discussion came to an abrupt end with the words, "Oh no, I would never date a coloured person."

Now I don't actually think she meant any offence by that statement. And with English as her second, maybe even third language, I suspect that she just lacked the vocabulary to express her views alternatively. But she'd already been trying our patience that evening so that was definitely the cue to leave. Which was a real shame, as I genuinely felt a spark with Sophie after my somewhat embarrassing opener.

It seemed my losing streak was set to continue.

As I walked back from the gents I crossed paths with her as she headed towards the ladies.

Sophie: "You guys aren't leaving are you?"
Me: "Yeah to be honest we were both getting a little frustrated with Elena anyway but her last comment just sealed the deal."
Sophie: "I know. I still can't believe she said that. Not least because it would rule out any chance of dating someone like you."

Ahhh yes. Your confidence and sheer determination in going after what you want. THAT was the thing that intimidated me about girls like you.

That being said... *Haaal-le-lujah, Haaal-le-lujah! Loki, I could kiss you.*

Now it may or may not surprise you to hear that I'm not too smooth at handling compliments (amongst other things). So for fear of fucking things up, I mumbled a thank you, suggested that she join us and pretty much ran away to inform Slacks of what had happened.

So after spinning some half-truths to Kate and taking advantage of the fact that it was getting late, Slacks, Sophie and I ditched the others and headed towards the West End.

Admittedly, he didn't really need to be there but we were at that crucial stage where Sophie was still deciding whether or not she wanted to sleep with me and dismissing him too early could be viewed as a sign of arrogance on my part; potentially blowing everything.

Conversely if he stuck around too long, there was a danger of it turning into three colleagues just having a drink. But thankfully he knew what he was doing and at around one o'clock we waved goodbye to him and jumped in a cab back to Sophie's place.

We didn't even make it to her bedroom and started making out on the living room couch. After around half an hour of fifteen-rated material there was a rustling of keys at the door.

Me: "I thought you said your flatmate wasn't going
            to be in?"
Sophie: "She shouldn't be?"

We quickly straightened ourselves out and waited for the door to open. "Oh my God Rosie, what's the matter?"

Her flatmate was a mess; mascara everywhere and tears streaming down her face. She managed a muffled, "Oh sorry, I didn't realise you had company," before running upstairs in a new flood of tears.

Sophie: "Sean, I'm so sorry. I need to go and check on her. Back in five minutes I promise."

Me: "Of course, don't be silly. I understand. Take as much time as you like." I lied fairly convincingly, hoping that the sensitive angle would curry favour later on.

True to her word she came back in five minutes, but this was only to tell me that Rosie was a complete wreck (it turned out she'd just broken up with her boyfriend – hence her return to the flat), that she'd probably need to stay with her for another twenty minutes and that she'd make it up to me afterwards.

I ignored most of what she said except for the part about 'making it up to me', which was when things started to go awry; as this just made me hornier than I already was.

Figuring her second session with Rosie would clearly be longer than twenty minutes and that in that time, I could safely bosh one out, remove all traces of the crime and still be good-to-go; I took my phone out and started looking up porn sites.

I recall settling on some fake casting-couch number but not much else after that…

Rosie: "OH. MY. GOD. That's revolting."

Sophie: "SEAN. Wake up!"

It turns out that I had failed to factor in how tired I was. And when the two of them returned to apologise for being so long; they found me sleeping upright, with my flies undone and my hand still cupping my then barely visible penis.

And the quest for sex with a posh girl continues.

★

Quite amazingly, the girls still let me sleep on the couch, which I presume they have since burnt or sold on Gumtree. Though given the events of the previous night, I didn't stick around too long in the morning; daring only to wash my hands in their kitchen sink before leaving (I was too scared to visit the bathroom as that required walking past their bedrooms).

Like a lot of guys, I kept a 'morning after' kit in the office and headed straight to my desk to collect my toothbrush and other items when I got in. My boss was already at his desk tapping away on his keyboard.

Boss: "You're in early."
Me: "I know. And there's a story behind it believe me. Let me just sort myself out first and then I'll fill you in."
Boss: "OK but before you go, what's that on your shirt?"
Me: "What?" I looked down to where he was pointing rather bemused. "Nooo."
Boss: "No way? Is that?"
Me: "Yes. Yes I believe it is mate."

I was grateful for three things that morning:

1. That only my boss had seen me (ignoring all the strangers I'd passed on the way in of course);
2. That it was Sophie's last day; and
3. That the 'morning after' kit included a spare shirt.

And I guess THIS is why they call him the God of Mischief.

#5

FORGET TO BOOK A ROOM AT THE HOTEL

il'N was probably the last of my chums to get married from our Saturday school (don't take the piss, I was forced to attend and had no say in the matter) and even though he and I had drifted a hell of a lot since those days, there was no way I was going to miss his wedding.

As somewhat of a recluse in our community, I remember hoping that I would just be able to slip into the crowd unnoticed and avoid the usual invasion of privacy that takes place in most things Tamil.

However my ex-wife and I had only separated around two years prior and reasons for the break-up were still a source of gossip for some.

[Oh yeah, I got married to and subsequently separated from my childhood sweetheart between #3 and #4. And whilst I'm happy to talk about most things, that's off-limits. For the record though, I screwed things up.

When my ex compiled her pros and cons list of being with

me, I'm sure that entry two or three in the right-hand column would've read something like, 'he's unable to keep details of our life together private'. So when she eventually discovers this book, I hope the irony of me finally being able to keep my mouth shut isn't lost on her.]

The wedding itself was textbook Tamil Hindu. I mean no disrespect by that but if you've been to one…

For those of you who have seen any Bollywood films, you're probably picturing wonderful colours, beautiful decorations, people dancing in the street to the drums and maybe even a token elephant, right? But in reality it's:

Bollocks, I've got to sit here with 499 other people listening to that incessant din. My nuts are practically glued to my thighs it's so hot. I don't know what's going on except that it's going to be at least three fucking hours before I can have a beer. And where's the elephant?

As with most weddings though, unless you're actually involved in the proceedings, the only part you really care about is the evening reception. And it was no different that day.

Unlike a few hours earlier, the embargo on alcohol and meat (standard procedure for Hindu ceremonies) had been lifted and the guest list had been culled to a more manageable 100 or so. Throw in some loose women and some music and it was just like a work social. Except I was struggling with the loose women and the crowd was almost entirely Tamil.

Well, that goes some way towards explaining the women situation I guess.

I'd quickly glanced over the seating arrangements for dinner when I arrived. None of the guys I'd met on the stag or knew from my Saturday school days were on my table, though I did recognise the names of two chaps I'd played rugby against back at school.

Maybe this'll be OK after all.

I didn't know either of them that well however, and once it emerged that they were quite religious and generally frowned upon my hedonistic lifestyle, our conversation became a little stagnant.

Upon realising that I was to spend the remainder of the meal with just my thoughts, I proceeded to get hammered on the seemingly endless supply of red and white wine; the biggest casualty of their chosen way of life? Alcohol.

By the time we'd finished and the first dance was over, I was suitably trashed yet still lucid enough to stay clear of the dance floor. So I just meandered near the exit chatting shit to anyone who would indulge me. That's when I noticed two, potentially single, attractive (and not just because I was drunk), white chicks – Vicky and Linda – talking to the bride.

Huh, this night may have just got interesting.

Vicky was from Essex but, unlike the stereotype, wasn't heavily reliant on make-up, a fake tan and false lashes; I wasn't sure about her tits though. She kind of reminded me of the TV presenter, Sofie Allsop, except for the accent of course. And Linda? Well, were it not for the fact that she was from Ireland, I would've said for sure that I was in the presence of Roxy from *Eastenders* that night. I was initially drawn to her but, who am I kidding, I would've gladly hooked-up with either one of them.

[By the way, I'm not implying for one second that I think all white girls are loose. My comment was more a reflection of my view that Tamil girls are generally very reserved and highly

41

unlikely to hook-up with a stranger at a wedding. And, in my defence, these two just radiated 'we're easy, come and get us'.]

Accepting that I required yet more Dutch courage before approaching the girls, I went back to the bar for a refill. Tweedledum and Tweedledee (a couple of guys not too dissimilar to me) were already there and had also clocked the evening's entertainment; who by now were within striking distance.

Now whether we approached the girls or whether they made a play for us, I can't remember. But how it materialised is academic as we were there and finally talking to them. Well… near them. The three of us were still complete pussies. Even when drunk.

Tweedledee's brother-in-law happened to join us at the bar and my reaction to seeing him for the first time in almost two years was to cup him by the balls. Don't ask.

On seeing me do this, I heard Vicky say, "Oh what a shame, the pretty ones are always gay aren't they?"

To which you would think my obvious response would've been something like 'who me? I'm straight; come out back and I'll prove it to you.' Not that I've got the balls to be that forward of course.

But instead, I played up to her current perception of me and with my best Boy George impersonation replied, "Well I do love cock."

Again, I have no idea what prompted me to do so but for the sake of this story, let's just blame everything that happened in the previous forty seconds on my two chums Gin and Tonic.

After cock blocking MYSELF, I retreated to the bar and continued to search for answers in the bottom of a glass. I was into my second or third conspiracy theory when Tweedledee came over to tell me that they were closing up and busses were waiting outside to take us to the hotel.

I didn't actually have a room booked but it was pounding with rain outside and I didn't fancy negotiating a cab on my own so I followed him out.

Once on the bus, I headed straight to the back to continue hypothesizing. Unbeknown to and luckily for me, the girls were staying at the same hotel and boarded the same bus. And even better; all the rows at the front were taken so Vicky ended up sitting next to me and Linda was across the aisle facing us.

This next part may have been my imagination but I'm sure Linda and I were eye-fucking the hell out of one another. *Maybe Vicky hadn't mentioned that I 'liked men' to her?*

The four of us were also finally engaging in conversation. That bastard Tweedledum had surfaced from somewhere.

Everything was going swimmingly until some amateur up front started to be sick. Sadly for the rest of us, he made no effort to find a window and the whole cabin quickly stunk of death.

Now the guys all think that this was a line but I'd say by now, you know that I'm not that calculated when it comes to talking to women. But I leant over to Vicky and said, "This may sound strange but would you mind if I smell your hair? I don't think I can handle the stench in here and your hair just smells so nice."

And she honestly replied, "Yeah sure, it's not like you're gonna try anything. After all, you're gay."

It was whilst resting my head on her shoulder, quite literally snorting her that I responded, "You do know that I'm not actually gay right?" And proceeded to kiss her neck.

I don't know what triggered that as my original motive was genuinely to avoid the smell. Plus I was convinced that I had laid the foundation for some Linda tap later. But what did I care? As after a few seconds of working her neck, Vicky started kissing me back and were it not for the other people on board, we definitely would have fucked on the bus.

The remainder of the journey was a bit of a blank but I mustn't have had to wait a long time in order to have sex with her, as my next clear memory was of her kneeling down next to a urinal in the men's room, giving me head. I told you she was easy.

I could see the back of her head in the mirror and, noting that she was concentrating solely on my cock, I couldn't resist doing a tribute to Christian Bale in *American Psycho* and started to point at myself in the mirror whilst winking and flexing my biceps. I know… what a cock / hero.

Scene 2 was me taking her from behind with her right leg straddled over the sink. Unlike me she chose to leave her clothes on. So it was your textbook skirt up from the back, knickers to the side job.

I can't remember if I came but Scene 3 was us back in reception and she wasn't in a rush to be elsewhere. So I'm guessing:

1. I didn't as I was too pissed;
2. I didn't as we were interrupted (that sounds familiar); or
3. I did but she wanted to go again.

We found Tweedledee seated by himself round the corner.

44

Me:	"Where's Tweedledum?"
Tweedledee:	"He's upstairs with Linda."

Bad Smithson: *What the fuck? How did that happen?*

Good Smithson: *What do you care? We got to tap the other one and barring a monumental balls up, I'd imagine we're set for the rest of the night too.*

Bad Smithson: *Yes. But we wanted to have sex with Linda and we saw her first.*

Good Smithson: *Firstly, that finders-keepers shit only works in the playground and secondly, we probably kissed goodbye to that when we tried to finger her friend on the bus!*

Tweedledee:	"Sean, are you OK? You looked like you were a million miles away."
Me:	"Huh? Yeah, sorry. No, I'm fine. Good for Tweedledum."

Good Smithson: *You lying bastard.*

Bad Smithson: *Fuck you Good Smithson. Who invited you anyway?*

Vicky:	"Tweedledee, why are you here though? Didn't they go to our room?"
Tweedledee:	"No, we all thought that you two had gone to your room. So I said I'd wait down here for an hour whilst they did their thing. If I'd have known you guys were in

45

the toilet, I could bloody be asleep by now."

Bad Smithson: *I hate to say it but that pussy Good Smithson is on to something. We've blown our chance with Linda. Now get your head back in the game and close this other chicken.*

Me: "Sorry man," – cue fake sympathy pat on the shoulder – "but one man's misfortune is another man's gain eh? Vicky, what say we head up to your room?"

Vicky: "Well we can't can we? As Linda will want to sleep there once she's done. Why can't we just go to your room?"

Me: "Erm… I don't actually have a room but wait here, I'm sure we can fix that." And I scurried off hoping that there was at least one spare room that night.

Receptionist: "Yes sir, we have a double room available. It comes with…"

Me: "Whatever. Great. I'll take it."

Now this should've been the part where I handed over my card, smiled at the guy and walked off, content in the knowledge that I was going to get some repeat action with a hot chick. However, I wasn't quite done sabotaging MY evening and taking the view that the seven steps to the men's room were seven too many, I decided to take a piss right where I was standing in the middle of the hotel reception.

Bet you didn't see that one coming, hey?

★

We've already established that I wasn't quite myself that night but to shed some light on my latest move we have to go back some years to '01. The setting? Perfect Fried Chicken, somewhere in South London.

As I'm sure you've all experienced yourselves on occasion, there are never any customer toilets in the smaller franchises. And clearly after a skinful, I was going to need a piss but it was far too busy outside to just go up against a wall. So on noticing that the counter top came up to just below my chest and that there were no other customers in the shop, I decided I'd try my luck.

There was a CCTV camera just above me to the right and I could actually see pieces of dirt being picked up from the white floor and moved backwards in the direction of the exit. No toilets, shit food and potentially some subsidence issues?

The guy behind the counter had absolutely no inkling. Nor did the new customers as they walked through my piss on their way towards the front.

I still haven't decided if I'm proud or ashamed of what I did that night but am pleased to say that I've finally grown out of that party trick. However in our prime, the guys and I marked some pretty wide ranging territories: bars, clubs, the student union, other fast food outlets, inside a moving cab (my chum was understandably thrown out straight away). And I'm fairly certain one guy even pissed on another guy!

Anyway now that you've got the background, let's fast forward back to '10.

★

Just like in '01, I leant in close to the counter and proceeded to have an uninspiring conversation with the receptionist whilst urinating; occasionally pointing my knob severely to the right or left to avoid a build-up of piss underneath my feet.

I shook myself off and smiled innocently at him as he gave me my room card. I was about to walk back to collect Vicky when a stranger who didn't even work at the hotel came marching through the entrance, shouting, "Stop that man, he just urinate all over the floor." The typo's intentional by the way.

In all the years I had engaged in these 'drive bys' not once had I been caught. Yet now, when there was guaranteed ploughing at stake (and the small fact that the entire wedding party was staying at that hotel and would most likely find out about what I'd just done), I had finally been rumbled.

Still I was grateful that no one else was around or had heard the guy. I just needed to figure out how the hell I was going to deal with this without being thrown out.

Bad Smithson: *What the fuck did I say earlier?*

Me: *Huh?*

Bad Smithson: *Get your head back in the game and close that chicken right? Yet somehow you heard, get your cock out and urinate all over the floor!*

Me: *I'm sorry OK. I don't know what's going on with me tonight. What the fuck do I do now though?*

Bad Smithson: Hmmm… I don't know. You've really fucked us here… Look there's only one thing for it. You're going to have to be ice cold like Andre 3000 and just bullshit like you've never bullshitted before.

Me: Roger that. I'll give it a shot. By the way, what happened to Good Smithson? I was half expecting him to say that I should just confess to what I did.

Bad Smithson: Yeah I thought he might do that too so I slipped him some roofies whilst you were pissing. He won't be bothering us for the rest of the night.

Me: "I'm sorry what?" And I turned to face my accuser.

Stranger: "There!" He pointed to an area of the floor now covered in my piss. "This is you. I saw you taking piss while smoking outside."

Me: "Nooo, I believe you're taking the piss with your poor command of the English language."

Feeling quite pleased with my insult and buoyed by Bad Smithson's encouragement, I pulled out my best Colin Firth from the repertoire, turned to the receptionist and said, "This is preposterous, do I look like the kind of man who would urinate in a hotel reception?"

As lowest common denominator as I must be sounding in this story, I actually scrub up pretty well in a suit and tie (successfully retrieved from the toilet).

Clearly the receptionist thought so too and wasn't even

going to bother getting out of his chair until the stranger reached over and grabbed him from behind the counter to show him what I'd done.

Receptionist:	"WHAT IS THIS?"
Me:	"I honestly have no idea. It must have been there before I got here."
Stranger:	"No! I saw him."
Me:	"I'm sorry, do you even work here?"
Stranger:	"No."
Me:	"OK. Well then this doesn't concern you does it?" *You potentially night-ruining, meddling prick!* "I think we can handle it from here." And I looked at the receptionist pleadingly for confirmation that this 'witness' didn't have to stick around.

Thankfully he felt comfortable enough dealing with me on his own and ushered the guy away from the crime scene.

To be fair to him, he'd done nothing wrong and certainly didn't deserve my abuse; neither then nor in this story. But there was random wedding sex at stake, which changes everything.

Receptionist:	"Sir, there is no way that this was here before and the other gentleman said that he saw you urinating so I'm afraid that I'm going to have to ask you to leave the hotel immediately."
Me:	"Wait, wait. Now I remember. I spilt my drink whilst you were behind the counter

	entering in my card details. Remember, I have paid for a room already."
Receptionist:	"Then where is your glass? And there is too much liquid here for one drink."
Me:	*Who the fuck is this guy? CSI Grissom?* "OK look, this is really embarrassing."

By the way, I still feel really terrible to this day about what I said next.

"But I wear one of those bags for people who can't use the toilet and it burst earlier. What that guy saw wasn't me urinating but actually me emptying my bag. I shouldn't have done it here I know but it just happened and I didn't know what to do? I'm sorry."

| Bad Smithson: | *Wow that really was ice cold. I'm impressed.* |
| Me: | *Thanks. Me too.* |

The receptionist and I stared at one another for the next thirty seconds; him trying to figure out if my bullshit was plausible and me trying to figure out if he had bought it. The fact that neither of us actually knew anything about those bags or how they work probably weighed in my favour so I thought I was home free.

Regrettably for me, we held one another's gazes for just a second or so too long and I burst out laughing.

51

Me: "OK, OK yes. I did piss on your floor.
                       Look, I'm really very drunk and I don't
                       know what came over me. But please. You
                       can't kick me out. There's a girl sitting on
                       the other side of that wall who wants to
                       have sex with me so I really need for you
                       to just be cool and let me stay here.
                       PLEEEEASE… I'll do anything."

Were it not for the piss directly below me, I would've gotten
down on my knees and offered to give him head but it looked
like it wouldn't be necessary as the guy was going to grant me
a reprieve.

Receptionist: "You know I really should throw you out.
                       But I will let you off this time."
Me: *Clearly another fan of random wedding sex.*
                       "Thank you, thank you, thank you."
Receptionist: "But you will need to pay to clean this
                       up."
Me: "Absolutely."
Receptionist: "So give me your card as I am putting
                       through a damages charge of £125."
Me: "What the fuck? £125? The room was
                       only £100. Hell, I'll get on my hands and
                       knees and mop it up with my jacket for
                       that price."
Bad Smithson: *Why are you arguing with him you fucking
                       moron? Shut the fuck up and pay the man so
                       we can have sex.*

| Receptionist: | "I am happy to just throw you out if you prefer?" |
| Me: | "Nooo… It's fine. Here's my card." |

As he busied himself putting through the bogus charge, I took a little comfort in the fact that £225 was still less than a 'Bunnies' girl (a story for if we ever meet in person) and judging by her performance in the toilet, Vicky was certainly on a par with one of them so this was, in fact, still a decent investment.

| Receptionist: | "All done sir." |
| Me: | "Cool thanks. And once again. SO sorry…" |

I'm fairly certain Vicky was asleep on the couch when I came back but all I really remember was rushing her onto the lift so we could get the hell out of there before anyone saw us. Tweedledee may or may not have been with us but that's kind of irrelevant.

So finally, around an hour or so after arriving at the hotel, we were actually alone.

I'd love to tell you that I banged the shit out of her for the rest of that night but I honestly have no recollection. I could have done that. Or I could have passed out. Or Tweedledee may have been with us in the lift and I could have banged the shit out of him. I just don't know.

#6

TRY TO SLEEP WITH HER BEST FRIEND

It turns out that I didn't bang the shit out of Vicky that night as I woke up extremely horny at around 4 am, but unfortunately she was still fast asleep. Accepting that if I tried to prod her any more than I was already doing it could be misconstrued by a jury, I decided to throw in the towel. Had I have known the Wi-Fi password for the hotel I would've jerked off right beside her.

And perhaps I should've done to avoid what actually happened.

With Good Smithson gone my moral compass was totally FUBAR. So after making certain that Vicky was out for the count, I slid out from under the sheets and started looking around the room for her handbag. Luckily it was on a table on my side of the room. I unzipped it and began to rummage around the contents inside: cards, shoes, cash – *hmmm… do I want to add theft to the rap sheet…? Nooo put it back* – lipstick, camera… bingo. Phone.

Still bitter at being thwarted by Tweedledum earlier that evening, Bad Smithson and I decided that we were going to make a house call to Linda's room. But we had no idea where that was. Yet.

★

Linda:	"Hey Vicky, what's up?"
Me:	"Oh no, it's not Vicky. It's Sean. Sorry for disturbing you, it's just that Vicky is quite drunk and I wanted to bring her back to your room if that's OK? What room number are you?"
Linda:	"Oh OK, yeah that's fine. It's room 213."
Me:	"Cool. See you in two."

I didn't want to make the same mistake I made back at Catherine's in '05 so this time I put some trousers on at least. *Knock, knock.*

Linda:	"Hey. Where's Vicky?"
Me:	"Yeeeah, about that." I invited myself into her room as I talked. "She's actually fast asleep upstairs in my room. So I was thinking that maybe you and I could…"
Linda:	"GET THE FUCK OUT OF MY ROOM RIGHT NOW!"
Me:	"I see…"

And no sooner had she opened the door for me, she slammed it shut again, narrowly avoiding my hand in the process.

Me:	*So I guess it doesn't really matter if I wear clothes or not, girls just clearly don't enjoy being woken up in the middle of the night to have sex with me.*

Bad Smithson:	*Huh? I did not see that one coming.*
Me:	*Me neither. She was totally giving me the come-on on the bus.*
Bad Smithson:	*Whatever man. Her loss. Now hurry back upstairs in case she decides to ring her friend and tell her what a weapons grade cunt you are!*
Me:	*Roger that.*

★

Before getting back into bed with Vicky I made sure to turn her phone off and placed her bag as far away as possible from the bed just in case she was tempted to check for messages in the morning.

At the time, I didn't actually feel that bad about what I'd attempted to do as the potential pay-off far outweighed the risk involved in my eyes. Plus if I played the remainder of my hand correctly, there was every possibility of tapping Vicky once more in the morning and swiftly disappearing without having to see either girl again.

The shame of it was, Vicky was actually a cool chick and I would like to have 'hit that on the regular' (sorry, I was listening to a lot of Drake when I wrote this) but there'd be no chance of that if Linda opened her mouth. Which, I'm sure she would've done eventually.

As I lay there trying to fall asleep I wondered just how many predicaments I could have avoided in my life if I'd just masturbated instead. I'd say pretty much all of them!

★

TRY TO SLEEP WITH HER BEST FRIEND

Vicky started stirring at around eight that morning and, what d'you know, I was still horny. I chose to deploy the same prodding strategy as before and eventually found myself on my knees straddling her as she sat up in the middle of the bed. As she switched between giving me head or a tit-wank, she asked me what I thought of her breasts.

Me:	"Yeah great, love them." By the way ladies, how else is a guy supposed to answer that?
Vicky:	"They're fake you know?"
Me:	*Well how about that? There IS some Essex in her.* "Really? I wouldn't have been able to tell." I seriously couldn't.
Vicky:	"I know right? My doctor's name was actually Mr Carver. So you can imagine how scared I was before I met him," she chuckled to herself. "But he's done a really good job I think."
Me:	"Love his work!" And shortly afterwards I spunked all over them.

As she was cleaning herself up she asked for my number. Thankfully I remembered just as she went to reach for her bag and suggested that I take her number down instead before quickly steering her out the door.

As cool as she was, there was a certain quality about her that suggested she had no problem punching a guy in the face if she really wanted to. So just in case, I got the hell out of there as quick as I could and went off in search of the boys.

They were already up and getting ready when I knocked on their door. But before we headed to breakfast, we had a very quick debrief.

Me: "Did you tap?"
Tweedledum: "Yeah. You?"
Me: "Yeah. Good?"
Tweedledum: "Yeah. You?"
Me: "Yeah."
Tweedledum: "Cool."
Me: "Cool." I told you it was quick.
Tweedledum: "She left all her jewellery here though man. What should I do with it?"

Keen to avoid any contact with the girls, I was about to suggest we steal it when there was a knock at the door.

Tweedledum: "Oh, hey."
Linda: "Yeah hi. I think I left my jewellery here last night?"
Tweedledum: "Oh yeah, we were just talking about that."
He returned promptly to fetch her stuff.

The door was ajar enough for us to make eye contact and she gave me this kind of 'I'm embarrassed about what I did last night but not as embarrassed as you should be' look. And I just nodded back at her in agreement, thankful that she hadn't exposed me.

We hung around in the room for a bit after she left in the hope that we might avoid them at breakfast. In the lift down

TRY TO SLEEP WITH HER BEST FRIEND

we tried to get our stories straight about what we were going to tell people if they asked.

It turned out that Linda was the bride's boss and Vicky was another work colleague so she probably didn't want to hear that two of her husband's friends had slept with them on her wedding night.

And of course although we had separated, I still didn't want news of me and Vicky to get back to my ex through the 'Tamil-vine'. So we decided we would just deny any involvement in anything.

I got out of the lift and as I entered the restaurant area I saw Vicky and Linda saying goodbye to the bride. *So close...* It was hard to read what she might have been thinking but I decided against striking up a conversation in case Linda had talked and my concerns over physical violence were valid; I would just follow up with a text later that weekend.

As I made my way to the breakfast buffet, quite a few people started to point and whisper amongst themselves. I didn't mind particularly as I was unlikely to see any of them ever again but it would have been nice to know which of the previous night's three scandals they were discussing.

Ignoring their glances and focusing my energy instead on maximising the small surface area of the plate, I almost didn't notice Lil'N as he walked up behind me.

Lil'N: "Big fan of everything. Even the pissing."
Me: "Oh my God, you know about that?"
Lil'N: "Know about it? I was there when the receptionist was trying to throw you out.

Pretty much everyone in the lobby saw you except for Vicky somehow?"

Me: "Holy shit. I don't remember any of this. I'm so sorry man."

Lil'N: "Listen, it's fine. But the wife definitely isn't pleased so you may want to lay low and just disappear quietly after you've eaten. We'll catch up properly once I'm back from the honeymoon."

And after another feeble attempt at an apology, we parted ways.

★

I decided to send Vicky an innocuous text the next day (Sunday) in the hope that nothing had been discussed between the girls.

I finally received this response the following Thursday: 'Yeah it was a great wedding, I had fun. Linda told me what you did. Don't text me again.'

Definitely wasn't worth the potential payoff!

★

About a fortnight after the wedding I was sitting next to my boss and an email popped up on my screen from my ex-wife. I hadn't heard from her in quite some time and my heart immediately started to race with panic.

Whilst neither of us were thinking about getting back

together, hearing that your former flame has been with someone else so publicly is never pleasant. I of course assumed that this was what the email was about.

After five or so minutes of pacing up and down I finally composed myself and clicked open. I'd already asked my boss to go and stand on the other side of the room as I wanted to be totally alone to digest the message.

'You urinated in the hotel reception?!?!?!'

"Ohh, is that all it is. Mate, it's nothing. You can sit back down."

The pros & cons of being with Sean

PROS   *CONS*

...

#2 – He can't keep his mouth shut

...

#4 – He still thinks pissing in public is funny!

#7

TAKE HER NUMBER DOWN INCORRECTLY

Guns wasn't actually leaving the firm but merely moving to another department internally so a big send-off wasn't even necessary. But he was off to join the investments team, who had a much higher density of private school cunts than our own department and we suspected that he would eventually become one too. He was born *The Only Way is Essex* but wishes he was *Made in Chelsea* so it was important to remember him how he once was.

We knew if we went to a strip club too early it would end badly for all our wallets so we just did as always; got drunk and left it to chance.

The night started off with the usual suspects plus a few faces from his new department but through a combination of paternal duties on Saturday morning, a healthy fear of strippers and just peaking too early; only Guns, Slacks and I actually made it to the club.

The pub trail we'd taken had led us towards Secrets, Covent Garden, which suited me perfectly as I probably spent too much time in the Holborn branch.

I had matured somewhat over the years and no longer pounced on the first girl to sit next to me. But being less acclimatised to this habitat than me or Slacks, it was safe to say that Guns was still a fan of this approach. And if I recall correctly, his arse had barely made an imprint on the leather seats before he was whisked off by some fake-breasted, Eastern European belle.

After shooting the shit with Slacks for a while, I decided enough was enough and went for an *'amuse-coq'* with a cute, young French girl. Plus we'd only given the stripper enough money for two dances so Slacks shouldn't have been waiting on his own too long.

A couple of friends from university claim to know a guy that actually took a stripper back to his place just by brazenly asking her. That, and about £400 they reckon; though I'm still unclear if this was including the money he'd already spent on lap dances or a further premium for sex. Either way, I decided that I would test this theory out with the French girl.

A friendly piece of advice; if you're going to try this, perhaps wait until you've established some sort of rapport rather than leading the conversation with it.

I returned swiftly afterwards to find Slacks humouring some poor girl he clearly had no interest in giving any money to. My arrival helped her figure this out and she left soon after.

Me: "Has Guns been back?"

Slacks: "No. He must be spunking his own money on that girl now I guess."

Guns was still fairly junior at that time (though that didn't dent his confidence one bit) and there was a marked difference between our salaries. Combine that with his desire to move out of his parents' house as soon as physically possible and some lingering student debts, and he had a strip club budget akin to mine back in '05. So the fact that he was still with this girl could only have meant that he'd fallen in love with her, which as you know, can happen to the best of us.

He joined us about five minutes later and couldn't wait to tell us how fantastic she was. "Great chassis and knew how to work it. Blonde, English…"

Me:	"Hang on a minute, the girl we gave the money to was Polish or something wasn't she?"
Guns:	"Oh yeah, she was. But after she'd finished I went off with this other one. So like I was saying… bar was just right, not too big or too small… she was probably in her late twenties, maybe into her thirties…"
Slacks:	"How much did you spend?"
Guns:	"Only £40. I would've kept going but a) I really shouldn't spend any more money and b) I reckon I can still make my last train. That being said, she was so hot I could just spend the rest and risk missing the train. I guess I could always withdraw more out and catch a cab if I'm totally screwed?"

The cogs stopped turning in his head at the sight of an absolutely stunning blonde walking towards our booth.

Guns: "Oh look, here she comes now."

Me: "Oh my God, Christina?" I started to panic
          thinking, *What if she remembers that I was the
          immature twat from a few years back who sulked
          when she went off with another guy?*

Guns: "Yeah, how did you know that?"

Me: "Mate I'm sure I fell in love with that girl
          about four or five years ago but she sacked
          me off for this guy who used to work in our
          department before you joined as he had more
          money than me."

Christina: "Hi Guns. Decided if you'd like that extra
          dance yet?"

She'd stopped just outside our booth and was leaning
forward so her elbows rested on the ledge parallel to Guns'
now perspiring face. Though I wasn't faring much better
myself.

Whilst I knew that he would certainly have liked that extra
dance, I also knew that watching me squirm may have proved
more entertaining.

Guns: "We were just talking about that actually.
          Why don't you come join us? Our friend
          Smithson here was just telling us that he
          thinks he may have known you in a former
          life." *Wanker.*

Christina: "Really?" She seemed intrigued but was
          really just sizing up whether I'd be a decent
          mark or not.

Me: "Erm yeah, did you used to work in the Holborn branch like four or five years ago by any chance?"

Christina: "Yeah, why? Oh my God, sorry. Do we know one another?"

Me: *Behave chaps. Behave…* "I wouldn't say we know one another as such but I met you there a long time ago with another guy. And you ditched me for him as I believe you thought that you would make more money dancing for him. Which you did incidentally but it still sucked."

Christina: "Really sweetie? That doesn't sound like something I would do." There were those puppy dog eyes again.

Be cool Smithson. Remember, she's just after your money. And she played you before.

Christina: "Especially to someone as good looking as you."

Guilty. As. Charged. She's clearly into me.

I started blushing uncontrollably, not just because of her comment but also because the boys were now practically in tears; especially Guns. It was like he thought she belonged to him and that she just said that to win me over. Sound familiar?

Christina: "I tell you what. Once I've finished this dance
               for your friend, why don't I come back and
               make it up to you?"

Me: *Make it up to me? Oh my God, scratch everything.*
               She clearly wants my cock. "Or we can just go
               for a dance now? Guns was just saying before
               you joined us that he had a train to catch,
               weren't you bud?" *Checkmate mother fucker.*

As I looked back, I couldn't help but empathise with Guns'
'what the fuck' expression and felt slightly terrible that I had
done to him exactly what John did to me a few years prior.
But oh well. All's fair in love and whores.

My intention was just to have a few dances but it seemed
my earlier comment about being ditched had actually
resonated with her, as Christina seemed to be working
overtime to 'make it up to me'.

Before too long that household topic of the private booth
came up. You'll recall that previously I lost out due to a lack of
funds but now the equation read something like:

Fairly respectable post qualification salary + decreasing
dependency on brasses + Amex card

=

Decent strip club kitty

So this was an absolute no brainer.

By the way, when they say private, they basically mean away
from the masses but there are still punters around that can see
you trying to 'get your inappropriate on'. Don't get me wrong,

I was having a great time but if there was any chance of doing something 'off piste'; it needed to be just the two of us. Meaning I had to go VIP.

Through various films I'd seen over the years, most notably *Go*, I'd always imagined that this would set me back a small fortune. But from memory, the Secrets VIP room was slightly more palatable at £200 an hour so when Christina suggested we go there my interest was certainly piqued. By that stage I'd spent all my cash – the daily withdrawal limit back then was £200 – and I'd put another £50 on my credit card.

If you visit the Secrets website, you can actually see the VIP lounges for some of the branches. Unfortunately there are no pictures for Covent Garden but the lounge is actually located downstairs. So on hearing that we would be on an entirely different floor, how do you think I responded? Even the brutal 20-25% surcharge for card payments couldn't stop me. Credit card spend was now up to £300.

I was pretty wasted after the 'complementary' bottle of champagne so can't remember exactly what happened down there though I have vague recollections of trying to get my cock out at one stage. But to be honest that could've been from any number of my escapades. My next clear memory of that night was being back in the main area of the club with my hand under Christina's skirt.

It was definitely into the early hours of Saturday morning by then and I had switched to water to try and sober up. Unfortunately I had no idea what my tab was up to but it must've been a fair way over £300. And I'd also blown through another £200 in cash as some arsehole had kindly reminded me that my debit card would work again after midnight.

To conceal what was going on, I'd draped my jacket over her lap but I'm pretty sure everyone knew what I was doing. I distinctly remember her being particularly proud of how smooth she was down there. And I have to say that at that moment, I finally understood what Fat Joe meant (on MTV Cribs) when he said that stroking his chinchilla fur jacket was the closest thing to touching private parts.

Obviously I took this as a sure-fire sign that she was up for coming back to my place and proceeded to put the wheels in motion.

Me: "So I know this place is open for a bit longer but I was thinking; why don't you come back to mine after?"

Christina: "Sounds like a great idea sweetie. Obviously I can't leave with you though?"

Me: "Of course."

Christina: "So why don't you take my number down and when we're finished here, wait for me outside and call me when you see me leaving." Like an obedient puppy, I got my phone out and entered her number; though something didn't feel right.

Me: "Hang on a minute. Is this really your number? I'm going to ring it."

Christina: "Well I don't have my phone on me, do I? You're just going to have to trust me."

Hmm. This girl has just taken hundreds of pounds from you, possibly more, and she's asking you to trust her…

Christina:	"Or I could just go home alone if you'd prefer?"
Me:	"No." *Please don't change your mind. I love you.* "I shouldn't have said anything, sorry." I was pathetic.
Christina:	"It's OK sweetie. Now where were we? Oh yeah, I believe you were about to order us some more drinks."
Me:	"Sure. What did you want?"

AND THE AWARD FOR BIGGEST IDIOT GOES TO.

★

I must've waited outside for at least twenty minutes initially. During which time, I saw a heap of girls leaving, either getting into cabs or making their way to their own cars; but no sign of Christina. I kept ringing her phone but no answer.

Instead of accepting the inevitable, I started to come up with plausible alternatives to the scenario:

1. She'd left her phone at home and somehow I'd missed her leaving the club;
2. I'd taken her number down incorrectly and somehow I'd missed her leaving the club; or
3. She never intended to meet me, the number she gave me was fake and she'd left via the back exit.

OK so (3) WAS the scenario but I had nothing to lose by investigating (2).

Now excluding the digits 0 and 7, there are 10^9 possible combinations for the remaining numbers of a UK mobile phone. I stopped dialling after fifteen.

It was around four in the morning and even the radio cab drivers had all gone home, which is when I finally raised my white flag in surrender. By then I was fairly sober and decided to see just how much she'd taken me for. I pulled a heap of receipts out of my inner jacket pocket, sat down on the pavement and started counting one by one: £40 drinks, £250 VIP room, £75 drinks, £400 I'm not sure what…

It took every ounce of strength I had not to cry but when I'd totted everything up, including the cash, I'd managed to spend £1,430. And I still had to get home!

But wait, it gets better.

Now remember, I wasn't the fucking Wolf of Wall Street. And whilst I was able to settle this beast, I felt particularly aggrieved as to how it had arisen and flatly refused to accept responsibility for it. So instead I did what any self-respecting man would do.

04:15 am

American Express:	"American Express, how can I help you?"
Me:	"Yeah hi, I'd like to report my card missing."
American Express:	"OK sir, when was the last time you had it?"
Me:	"Hmm. Well I recall paying for some drinks in one of our locals at around 6 pm but didn't use the card again after that."

American Express: "OK sir, I've put an immediate block on it."

Me: "Thank you. Gee, I really hope it hasn't been used for anything. Although now that I think about it, I did notice some guys looking over my shoulder when I was entering my pin." *Smithson you old fox you.* "You can't see if there have been any transactions since can you?"

American Express: "There was £18.30 at The Bank of England."

Me: "Yes, that's the local. That's OK."

American Express: "I can't see anything else at the moment."

Me: "Thank goodness for that." *Shit, maybe none of the transactions went through somehow?* "But hypothetically speaking, what do I do if there are any 'fraudulent transactions'?"

American Express: "Well you'd have to wait until your statement came through and raise any queries you have with us then."

Me: "Ah OK, I see. Thanks for all your help."

04:20 am
Smarter than the average Smithson. Smarter than the average.

As there were no longer any radio cabs loitering, I made my

way down Kingsway in the hope of catching a black cab. But I needed to stop off at the cash machine first.

"FUUCK TO THE POWER BALLS!"

I'd already reached my daily cash limit on my debit card and had unwittingly just blocked my only other card. This was now officially the worst night of my life.

At my fittest, it took me around forty-five minutes to run the five and half miles from the office back to my flat in Earl's Court. But given my attire wasn't befitting of a lengthy hike and more importantly that I just wanted to lay there and be run over, I figured it would take me closer to two and a half hours to walk back home.

As it turned out, it took me closer to two and I finally got in at around half past six on Saturday morning.

★

The events of the previous night/earlier that morning were still weighing on my mind and I woke up around half nine in search of a snack to take my mind off things. As I stood in my kitchen surveying my limited options for breakfast, lunch and dinner that day given the self-inflicted credit crunch, my phone started to ring.

I didn't recognise the number so ignored it and hoped the caller would leave a voicemail if necessary. There was no voicemail but a text soon followed:

'Who the fuck is this?! I do not appreciate being woken up at four in the fucking morning!' OK, well I guess that wasn't Christina's number then either was it?

That wasn't the only call or message I would receive that day but it was certainly the most irate.

At around midday I had an unexpected call from Poitier. He was going to be in the area later on and wanted to know if I was around for some beers. Seeing as he would be buying all the rounds, I figured I owed him an explanation.

He found it all rather amusing until the part about the Amex call.

Poitier: "Smithson, quick question. Is that a new card?"
Me: "No why?"
Poitier: "Well, and this is just a thought, I would imagine that the fraud team at Amex would look into your regular spending habits before assessing any refund claims, wouldn't you?"
Me: "Yeees, carry on."
Poitier: "And if I know you as well as I think I do, I would place my life on the fact that not only have there been transactions on your card from Secrets in the past, there are probably transactions from all the bars you visited along the way?"
Me: "Hmm, go on."
Poitier: "And given that you work for an FSA regulated firm and probably want to continue doing so, I would also think that you wouldn't want to be convicted of credit card fraud now would you?"
Me: "Hmm, let me call you back."

12.15 pm

American Express: "American Express, how can I help you?"

Me: "So… Funny story…"

Karma… She's definitely a bitch. As is Christina.

#8

Have 'some' standards

I t was the summer of '10 and somehow I'd been convinced to join a number of the ex-players from our year to take part in an old boys' rugby tournament that September.

After many failed attempts we had our inaugural training session in Green Park around July. As you can imagine with a bunch of out of shape twenty-eight-year olds, training didn't last too long so after about an hour and a half of falling on the floor and dry heaving, we were at a pub across the road from the station knocking back some beers.

As it was a school night we decided to wrap things up around 10 pm. Plus we were tired of being laughed at for looking like complete twats in our mud-stained kits. That's right, we had kits. We were never going to win the tournament but we had to look the part, right?

*

My folks' place was still listed as my main contact address so I hardly ever got any mail. But when I walked through the main entrance of my building that night I noticed a small envelope addressed to the occupier of Flat 2, 22 XXX Road, Earl's

Court. The same envelopes were in the letter trays for flats 1, 3 and the basement. I opened mine up.

'Dear resident,

I regret to inform you that the owners of Flat 2c, 24 XXX Road, Earl's Court are currently operating a sex trade from their premises. I cannot say how I came to know about this but I felt it was my duty to let you know. As a concerned resident of the area, I feel that we must group together to put an end to this filthy practice and shut the place down.'

Now the fast ones amongst you should've realised that No. 24 was next door. So maybe it was the sheer excitement of having just found out that my neighbours were hookers, or perhaps it was because I was slightly drunk, but without any hesitation, I grabbed the other letters and screwed them up. Still in my gear from before, I walked straight back out the door, side-stepped over the partition railing and pressed the buzzer for 2c.

As I waited for a response I remember thinking three things:

1. *That was quite a good note, concise and to the point. Clearly the author is fairly educated;*
2. *How awesome is this? Me, a seasoned whoremonger living next door to a brothel. Just think of the potential savings in admin costs; and*
3. *What the hell am I going to say if someone answers the buzzer?*

Intercom: "Hello, can I help you?"

Me: "Actually I think it is I that can help you."

Intercom: "I'm sorry, what? Did you make a booking?"

Me: "No but I think you're going to want to let me in as I have some information that you may find interesting."

Intercom: "Who is this? What do you want?"

Me: "Look, I live next door. Please, just let me in and I'll explain everything."

After a few seconds the buzzer sounded and I let myself in. The same letters were in all the trays for this building too. Even for Flat 2c. I take it back; the author was clearly a fucking retard!

I grabbed all the letters and proceeded up the stairs. The residents (or madams) of 2c were waiting for me in the outside corridor. Understandable I guess, given the circumstances.

Me: "Hi, Sean Smithson." I made a native Indian 'how' type gesture with my right hand. "BIG. FAN. OF YOUR WORK."

Madam 1:   "Erm. How is it that we can help you?"

Me: "Ah yes. I think you'd better take a look at these."

Madam 1:   "Hmmm… Oh my God. Those sneaky bitches."

Madam 2:   "Who do you think it was?"

Madam 1:   "It must be those Thai bitches from XXX Road."

Madam 2:   "Oh yeeah. They've been jealous of our gig for a while now."

They continued to have a conversation amongst themselves, somewhat oblivious to the knight in shining armour that had brought news of this propaganda to their attention. Not quite the hero's reception I was expecting. Though at least I had ascertained that there were some 'Thai bitches' in the area too.

Me: "Ahem."
Madam 1:   "Oh, I'm so sorry. Thank you for letting me and Sam know about this. My name's Liz by the way."
Sam: "Yes, you're a star. Come inside. I'll put the kettle on."

Put the kettle on? This is awesome. And I followed them in, still beaming with excitement at the prospect of what was on the other side of the door.

The first thing I noticed when I walked in was how tiny the place was. The owner of Flat 2 had actually converted it into three smaller units and 2c was where my living room would've been. Quite how they'd done it, I'm not sure but somehow they'd managed to create two rooms, a kitchen and a bathroom in that space. Throw in the balcony and it actually wasn't that bad.

After a very quick tour, I followed Sam into the kitchen and sat down.

Me: "So like I was saying. I'm a supporter of what you do and thought it was in everyone's best interests that I let you know as soon as possible. You'll be pleased to know that I destroyed the

	other letters in my building. If I could've, I'd have broken into all the other flats in the area and stolen their letters too."
Liz:	"Oh aren't you sweet."

Yes. That was me. Mr Sweet. Offering to break in and steal people's post in order to prevent a brothel from being shut down. Just the kind of guy every girl wants to take home to mum and dad.

We talked for around fifteen minutes. The main topics of discussion being:

1. How long they'd been operating for;
2. Who else the culprit may have been; and
3. What they were going to do about it.

I soon realised that I didn't really care about any of this and during a natural lull in the conversation I asked if anyone was actually working.

"Lillyyy!" shouted Sam. "Get up honey. We've got a customer."

I followed her into a small bedroom and sitting up on the bed was an attractive, yet fairly knackered looking, Thai girl. *Hmm. I guess I may not need to go to XXX road after all.*

"It's £40 for thirty minutes, £70 for sixty minutes. But seeing as you've been so helpful, you can have her for the full hour at £40."

Now this is more like the way to thank a hero, is what I should have been thinking. However in the whoring game, there are two things one must be mindful of when it comes to the transaction.

Firstly, always be suspicious of girls that offer thirty minute sessions. As over a given timeframe, they could potentially be turning over twice as much cock as their one hour peers. Ergo more chance of your Johnson falling off if you use them.

And the second golden rule? Always heed caution if the one hour price (or pro rata equivalent) is less than £100. If they are willing to service you for less, they must be desperate. Which means they are amenable to sleeping with all sorts and have quite possibly contracted all sorts. Once again placing your Johnson in potential danger, as an acquaintance of mine found out first hand.

Nottingham (summer '04)

After hearing that Nottingham University had the highest ratio of girls to boys in the country, a few of us decided to pay our friend Tom – who was studying there at the time – a visit.

Now although the ratio suggested that the odds were stacked in our favour, there was no adjustment for lack of game or standard of girl. So after a third successive night of no action, I found myself wondering along Forest Road (a shady area fabled for its street hookers) with Tom's friend, Ed.

Having walked up and down the road to no avail, we were just about to leave when a cab pulled up a few feet in front of us and out stepped a lady dressed in a cheap looking white suit. She walked in front of us for a few minutes without making eye contact.

Ed: "Dude, do you think she's a brass?"
Me: "Shut up Ed. She can fucking hear you." I was worried that we may offend her.

Ed:	"Well I think she is and I'm gonna find out." At which point Ed walked ahead to catch up with her… "Excuse me, do you have the time?"
Potential brass:	"Yeah, it's just gone one." Long, excruciating pause… "Are you boys looking for some action by any chance?"
Ed:	"I knew it! See Smithson, I told you she was a brass." *Nice Ed. Way to build up the girl's self-esteem.*
Confirmed brass:	"So I take it that's a yes then?"

After commencing the bidding at £10 for head, they eventually settled on £30. For everything! Now even if you've never done this sort of stuff before, you've got to know that that just doesn't sound right. I suggested to Ed that we just go home (by this stage, I had decided jerking off was a better option) but he was having none of it.

After an awkward session down a nearby alley, which included her answering her phone to another client mid blowjob and Ed suggesting that my 'homosexuality' was the reason I wasn't keen to partake, we jumped in a cab back home.

It was whilst fumbling around trying to find his keys that Ed noticed both his hands were stained in blood.

Ed:	"Urgh!! What the fuck is this!" He was waving his palms directly in front of my face.

Me: "I don't fucking know but I'd appreciate it if
            you didn't fling those things in my direction!"
            I seriously contemplated jumping out of the
            moving cab just to ensure he didn't touch me.

After a few seconds of staring at one another in disbelief, he finally
composed himself and drew his hands in to take a closer look.

Me: "Maybe she was on her period. You did wear
            a condom right?"
Ed: "Yeah of course."
Me: "OK let's just calm down then. Tom must keep
            some bleach or something downstairs. When we
            get in, douse your hands – and probably your
            cock – in that stuff before having a shower.
            There must be a clinic near the university where
            you can get yourself checked out in the
            morning." And we both got out of the cab and
            didn't speak about the incident again.

I happened to see Ed a couple of years later on the tube and
am pleased to report that he didn't catch anything that night.
But the moral of the story is: if a girl is only going to charge
you something in the low double figures – please, get the fuck
out of there.

★

Given what you've just read, it probably won't surprise you
that my immediate thought of Sam's offer was, *At £40 for one*

hour, my penis is pretty much guaranteed to fall off afterwards! No wonder she looks so knackered.

Me:	"Erm… Do you know what?" And I moved closer, lowering my voice to a whisper so as not to offend Lilly. "I've just remembered that I've got a really early start tomorrow so I should probably give it a miss actually. But perhaps another time?"
Sam:	"Suure, no worries. Whatever night works for you dear."

So it turned out that living next door to a brothel wasn't as great as I thought it would be. And like in any well run business, your pricing strategy is just as important as your location.

Still, it wasn't a total bust as I was invited back for a cuppa whenever I liked.

#9

ORDER THE HOT WINGS
BEFORE YOUR DATE

ince separating from my ex-wife, I've only really 'dated' one girl. 'Really? But you seem like such a catch Sean.' I know, right?

OK, so I get that a large part of this is self-inflicted but at the same time, there were girls whom I would've loved to have seen again but, for whatever reason (mainly because the feeling wasn't mutual), things didn't work out. Caroline was the exception.

Remember how I'd previously mentioned that Northern Monkey had teed me up with that line from *How I met your Mother*? Well it was with her. And such was his commitment to my cause that night that he even came back to her place to ensure that her friend – who was from out of town and staying with her – wouldn't throw a spanner in the works.

And by that I don't mean that he hooked-up with her. He simply kept talking to her whilst Caroline and I were making out in the corner until she eventually passed out on the bed.

I didn't actually sleep with her that night. I wanted to of course but she was having none of it. Partly because she wasn't that sort of girl but partly because her friend had relegated us to the living room couch. And I'm sure 'that' would've violated acceptable hygiene rules when you're living with six other women. Six other men; I'm not so sure?

So the next morning when she asked if I was actually going to call her, I responded, "Yes." Not just to get into her pants – though this did happen the next time we met – but also as there was just something about her.

Unfortunately the timing wasn't great. And due to a month long holiday that she'd planned before we met and a return up North for Christmas, I only saw her twice in the two months that followed. But we stayed in touch the whole time and not only was I really excited to see her again in January, I was even beginning to think, *Maybe this could go somewhere.*

I forget now who we'd played but Arsenal had won the early KO game that Saturday and my instructions were to pick up two bottles of wine before heading to hers. Luckily there's a Tesco Express opposite Gloucester Road tube station. There's also a KFC.

So after confirming my wine selection with her, I popped in for an *amuse-bouche* (a Fillet Tower box meal) before the main course. Of SEX.

Now in addition to being fairer than most Tamils, not having hair like a Lego character and not being able to speak our language; the other telltale sign that I may in fact be the milkman's son, is that I have a very low tolerance for spicy food. And although I knew it could lead to trouble later on, the Asian in me just couldn't let the hot wings go to waste.

Caroline's place was only five minutes away from the station and I was conscious that she might be wondering where

I was. But after the beers at the football, I couldn't take any chances and nipped downstairs to take a leak.

Noticing there was no one else in the gents I decided that was also an opportune moment to relieve some wind as I was feeling a little bloated after my feast.

It seems that the Colonel might have been lying all these years and may also have hailed from South Asia. That or my stomach was way more sensitive than I'd realised, as within seconds I'd managed to shit myself.

Thankfully I hadn't put my back into it. But I'd lifted my right leg off the floor ever so slightly for comfort, meaning some debris had reached some places it really shouldn't have.

I squeezed my butt-cheeks together as tightly as possible once I'd realised what had happened and contemplated my next move. I needed to get to the cubicle post-haste but was also very conscious of doing further damage. So much like the way Spiderman moves along an apartment windowsill when he's searching for the bad guys, I carefully side-stepped my way to freedom.

There was no time to dither and I simply went for it Shit Break style; complete with shudders, squeals and the occasional knee jerks.

Thirty minutes, five flushes and numerous tears later, the evacuation was complete. Don't quote me on this but the radius of the toilet roll was about 10cms when I got there and around 7.5cms when I was done. But as if what I'd gone through wasn't bad enough, I still had to clean myself up and make it to Caroline's, who by then had rung me three times.

I'm not sure how many of you have been in similar situations as an adult but trying to manoeuvre your way out of shit soaked underwear is no easy task, as not only does one need to avoid contact between turd and skin but also between turded clothes and non-turded clothes.

Slipping my trainers off was easy enough. My jeans on the other hand were a lot trickier; especially as they were bunched up around my ankles with my boxers. Yet somehow I managed it without any visible transfer.

I couldn't handle the thought of my bare feet potentially coming into contact with anything so kept my socks on as I lifted my feet up off the floor and carefully slid my boxers off, flicking them as far away as possible from me, which in reality was only about 50cm.

I don't know if the person on cleaning duty that day will ever read this story but all I can say is: Sir / Ma'am, I truly am so sorry for what I put you through and if you can prove to me that you were that person, I'd like to take you out for dinner. Though not at KFC.

Even though I'd successfully 'disposed' of my boxers I was still very concerned that there might actually be shit on me and, though incredibly risky, I took the decision to exit the cubicle and 'wash myself' at one of the sinks. And by that I mean, throw handfuls of water onto my thighs and butt-cheeks and run back inside to dry myself off with the remaining 7.5cms.

Sorry, but I'd like you to take some time to picture just how awful this situation was. I mean there I was; a grown man, sneaking around a KFC toilet in only a jumper and socks, throwing water on his nether regions.

All I can say is, thank God a kid didn't walk in as there's a strong chance you wouldn't even be reading this story on

account of my being in fucking jail! But I figured I'd made
Caroline wait that long. The least I could do was turn up not
looking like shit. Literally.

So after the most nerve-racking minute of my life and a
couple more flushes, I was finally 'ready' for my date.

I called Caroline straight away to explain the delay, siting a
very important call from a family member. In an ideal world I
would've told her the truth and the first thing I'd have done
when I got to her place would be to take a shower and burn
my clothes. But clearly this wasn't appropriate behaviour for a
fourth date (third really, if you think about it).

So when it eventually got to the part where we'd be doing
the 'Wild Thing', my hope was that it'd be with the lights off
and my clothing preferably buried somewhere on the other
side of the room. But you know what they say about the best
laid plans.

I don't know if it was just because we hadn't seen one
another in over three weeks but we completely skipped the
pleasantries and started going at it on the staircase up to her
room.

Me: "Erm, shouldn't we probably go to your
              room?"
Caroline: "It's OK, my flat mates are all out." And with
              that she pushed me up against a wall in the
              landing before ordering me to take my jumper
              off.

Now on the previous occasions we'd been together the sex was
good but it was fairly vanilla. And getting head wasn't even

remotely on the cards. So when her mouth started moving downhill, so too did my earlier plans. *Fuck it. You're about to get your dick sucked.*

I still recall her surprise upon noticing that I wasn't wearing any underwear and I dismissed it with a truly awful line that I just can't bear repeating. However it seemed to do the trick as she quickly returned to unfastening my buttons and pulling my jeans down. All that was left for me to do was, well… nothing really.

I was just like Clinton all those years ago with Lewinsky, except there seemed to be a distinct lack of sucking. And when I peered down to investigate, Caroline was actually underneath my cock, seemingly fascinated by something on the floor.

Although I had a fair idea of how this might end, I played dumb and asked her if everything was OK? To which she responded, "Oh God, I think I'm going to be sick," before running down the stairs to the bathroom.

With her head no longer obstructing my view, I leant forward for a better look and running down the back of my right, WHITE sock was a solid streak of turd.

I was wrong. This relationship wasn't going anywhere.

#10

Try to give her career advice

The bell for last orders sounded and once again we found ourselves in that precarious position of wanting to carry on drinking but not wanting to go to a nightclub to do so. The obvious solution? Secrets.

It stayed open well into the early hours of the following morning and the music never reached a level that proved intrusive to conversation. The fact that there were naked girls everywhere was merely the icing on the cake to my suggestion.

It was fairly empty for a Thursday night – both in terms of girls and guys – but there were still enough women around to keep Swirly and Woody entertained. They weren't regular drinking buddies of mine (probably because they worked in sales and were always out schmoozing) but I'd always had a good time with them previously.

After the Christina incident, I was extremely cautious about getting private dances. And by that I mean; I'd learnt absolutely nothing from the experience. However that night, I was quite content to just get drunk and laugh at someone else for a change.

Noticing that I was by myself, a cute brunette called Rachel walked over and pulled up a chair beside me.

Rachel: "This seat's not taken is it?"

Me: "No, knock yourself out."

Rachel: "So, did you want a dance?"

Me: "No, I'm alright for the moment, thank you."
            At which point I was expecting her to go off
            in search of another sucker or try to convince
            me to buy a dance for one of the others. But
            her reaction surprised me.

Rachel: "Do you mind if I just sit here with you then?"

Me: "No problem. But erm, don't you want to see
            if any of the other guys in here are interested
            in a dance?"

Rachel: "I've already been round twice. It's really
            quiet."

Normally that line would've melted my heart but I was
determined not to crumble so easily this time. Though she did
seem like a really sweet girl, so the least I could do was have a
conversation with her. Plus, well… you know?

A few years previously, I'd seen a documentary about
the Spearmint Rhino in London and one of the things it
revealed was that any girl who danced there paid an upfront
fee of £80 per night and had to dance on the main stage at
least three times. However any money they received from
private dances was entirely theirs to keep. Equipped with
this insider knowledge, I decided to enquire into Secrets'
policy.

Rachel: "Yeah, it's the same for us actually."

Me: "So… have you broken even tonight?"

Rachel: "No, I'm actually down for the evening."
            Which admittedly could have been some
            reverse psychology, Jedi mind trick but was also
            entirely plausible given the crowd.

Me: "And how many nights a week do you work
            here?"

Rachel: "Every night from Monday to Friday"

Me: "Are those nights any better?" I tried to be
            considerate, though already had a fair idea
            what her answer might be.

Rachel: "It's not that great at the beginning of the
            week but it usually gets better by Friday."

Still unwilling to pay for a dance (let alone the eight or so that
were clearly required to dig her out of that week's hole) but
genuinely 'thinking' that I wanted to help her in some other way,
I tried to steer the conversation towards other lines of work.

Me: "So you must do something else outside of this
            surely?"

Rachel: "I do some waitressing shifts in a café from
            time to time but mostly I just sleep during the
            day."

Me: "Hmm. Do you even like stripping? As maybe
            you're better off working in the café full time?"

Rachel: "Not really, no. I have thought about asking
            for more shifts at the café but the money's not
            that great."

Better than owing money though surely, I thought to myself, still trying to figure out if she was stupid or just confused about what she wanted in life.

Maybe it was the drink. Maybe it was because I just can't help myself. Or maybe because, in spite of all my stories, I can sometimes be quite a sweet guy. But I ended up suggesting that she apply for a job at my firm.

Admittedly, I didn't even know if there were any vacancies. And although maths was evidently not one of her strong points, she seemed as qualified as our secretary, Sue, who frankly didn't seem to do anything except refuse to work when I asked her or suck senior management cock from time to time (figuratively speaking of course).

I did some more digging and found out that she was comfortable using MS Office (which put her on a par with Sue in my opinion) and that she'd previously worked as a sales assistant in addition to the waitressing gig (so had experience in dealing with people, thus placing her above Sue).

Me:	"Look, I can't guarantee anything at all. But I see no reason why you couldn't apply for an administrative role at our firm."
Rachel:	"Oh my God, thank you so much. So should I give you my details or do you want me to take yours?"
Me:	"Erm, I don't have any cards on me (I mean seriously, who goes round telling people they're a tax adviser) but I tell you what…" and I distracted Woody from some double Ds just long enough to grab one of his, "why

don't you drop Woody a line and we'll see what we can do?"

You can always count on someone in sales to have a card.

★

Now unfortunately that entire exchange was much like the majority of conversations I have when I'm drunk. And although it seems to the other party(ies) that I am totally coherent and aware of my actions, I'm usually not and by the next morning I have pretty much little to no recollection of what I'd said or done.

So you can imagine my shock when returning to my desk after lunch the next day, I found the following forwarded message in my inbox:

'Dear Woody,

I met you and your friend John last night at the club. John told me to get in touch with him about job opportunities at your firm. I would therefore be grateful if you could pass this email onto John along with my CV (attached).

Thanks,
Rachel'

Three things immediately sprang to mind:

1. *Who the fuck is John?*

2. *Clearly she's not familiar with pronouns; and most importantly*
3. *What have I done?*

As if the poor girl emailing me with the genuine belief that a) there was a job and b) I could help her get it wasn't bad enough; Woody had copied in about twenty other guys, so you can understand what it must've been like in the office that Friday afternoon.

Amongst the more comical suggestions of what to do next was Guns' idea that I set up an interview between the two of them, with him playing the part of someone from HR. However as he would probably be unable to keep a straight face or his hand out of his pocket the entire time, we decided against it.

After deliberating for around an hour and deciding that I may have been onto something in my pissed up state the night before – and also just wanting to do the right thing by this girl – I emailed HR enquiring into current or upcoming vacancies.

Whilst replacing Sue was unfortunately not an option, there were at least two support roles she could've had a slim shot at. But before passing her CV on, I sought further consultation with my boss.

He pointed out that whilst Rachel's previous line of work shouldn't have to be an obstacle to her joining the firm, people would eventually find out – most probably from me and most probably before she'd even come in for an interview – which could make things uncomfortable for her if she ever got the job. And given the firm's history, if the news ever made it back to the powers that be that I was the one who teed up the move, I'd probably be blacklisted for the rest of my time there.

If only I'd known I was going to quit a year later!

So, I ended up texting her saying there was nothing available at the time but that we'd bear her in mind for the future. I couldn't ask her out after that, could I?

But Rachel, if you ever happen to read this story and are still in need of a job then get in touch. As you never know; this book 'could' lead to me being in a position where a) I need a secretary and b) I can actually afford to pay for one. Or failing that, we could just have sex? Your call.

Aaand that's #11.

Glossary

The following is a list of terms that may be foreign to you. The majority can be cross referenced on Urban Dictionary but in some cases, the meanings are unique to me and the guys.

Bar (or T-Bar) – tits / breasts; originating from the US word titty-bar meaning a strip club

Bolloxed – really drunk

Boshed – pretty drunk

Brass – whore / hooker

Drives – generic term for a driver of an unlicensed cab

Fit – attractive

Flat packed – the state of a man's balls after ejaculation: 'if you play this right, your nuts should be totally flat packed by the end of the night.'

FUBAR – Fucked up beyond all recognition

Googly – actual meaning is an off break bowled with an apparent leg-break action (cricket) but can also mean misdirected / mislead

Hand-shandy – a hand job

Johnson – US slang for cock / penis

Mathematics – sex; originating from the concept of putting 1s in 0s

Parkers – an awesome strip club in London

Recky – a reconnaissance mission

Secrets – a chain of strip clubs in London

Spec – type / preference

Tap – bang / sleep with / have sex with